Colossians and Philemon— The Epistles of Truth and Love

This is a self-study course designed to help you discover for yourself, from the Bible, some important basic truths concerning Colossians and Philemon

how to study the lesson

1. Try to find a quiet spot free from distractions and noise.

2. Read each question carefully.

3. Look up the Scripture reference given after each question. Make sure you have found the correct Scripture passage. For example, sometimes you will find yourself looking up JOHN 1:1 instead of I JOHN 1:1.

4. Answer the question from the appropriate Bible passage. Write, in your own words, a phrase or sentence to answer the question. In questions that can be answered with a "yes" or "no" always give the reason for your answer . . . "Yes, because. . . ."

5. If possible, keep a dictionary handy in order to look up words you don't understand.

1

6. Pray for God's help. You *need* God's help in order to understand what you study in the Bible. PSALM 119:18 would be an appropriate verse for you to take to God in prayer.

7. *Class teachers using this course for group study will find some helpful suggestions on page 47.*

how to
take the self-check tests

Each lesson is concluded with a test designed to help you evaluate what you have learned.

1. Review the lesson carefully in the light of the self-check test questions.

2. If there are any questions in the self-check test you cannot answer, perhaps you have written into your lesson the wrong answer from your Bible. Go over your work carefully to make sure you have filled in the blanks correctly.

3. When you think you are ready to take the self-check test, do so without looking up the answers.

4. Check your answers to the self-check test carefully with the answer key given on page 48.

5. If you have any questions wrong, your answer key will tell you where to find the correct answer in your lesson. Go back and locate the right answers. Learn by your mistakes!

apply
what you have learned
to your own life

In this connection, read carefully JAMES 1:22-25. It is only as you apply your lessons to your own life that you will really grow in grace and increase in the knowledge of God.

Introduction to Colossians

Ephesians and Colossians together represent one of the fullest, richest presentations of Christianity. There are many similarities between the two books. Out of 95 verses in Colossians, 78 have a marked resemblance to statements in Ephesians. Out of 155 in Ephesians, 78 resemble statements found in Colossians.

In Ephesians the Church is the primary object and the theme of the book leads up to Christ as the Head. In Colossians Christ is the primary object and the thought passes downward to the Church as His Body.

The Son of God is presented in Colossians as the Head and Cause of the whole created universe. The epistle is directed against false teaching and wages war on everything legalistic and materialistic.

Paul wants to visit the Colossians sometime later, but takes this occasion to warn them against errors of doctrine and practice. He sends the letter to them by Tychicus (4:7-9) who seems to be accompanied by Onesimus (Philemon 10-12).

Outline of Colossians (Lessons 1 to 6)

Concern for the Christians

1:1-15

Paul's Salutation

1. To whom is the epistle directed?

1:2 _____

2. What would lead one to believe that Paul must have had a wide ministry of intercession?

1:3 _____

3. State one request that Paul made for the believers in Colosse?

1:9 _____

_____

4. What other prayer was prayed for the Colossians?

4:12 _____

A Gospel of Hope

5. How did the Colossians regard other believers?

1:4 _____

6. What was the result of the gospel coming to the Colossians?

1:6 _____

7. While there is no evidence that Paul had visited Colosse, from whom did he learn much about these believers?

1:7, 8 _____

8. For what were the Colossians especially noteworthy?

1:8 _____

A Prayer for the Church

9. How does one become filled with the kind of spiritual wisdom which the apostle desired for these believers?

1:9; II Timothy 2:15 _____

_____

10. To whom should we go for spiritual wisdom and guidance?

Psalm 32:8 _____

11. Who must produce and sustain this knowledge?

I Corinthians 2:9, 10 _____

12. Why cannot this wisdom be classed as human wisdom?

I Corinthians 2:12 _____

13. What capacity does the unsaved person have for "spiritual understanding?"

I Corinthians 2:14 _____

14. What is the true aim of such spiritual understanding?

1:10 _____

_____

15. What does fruitfulness unto the Lord bring with it?

1:10, last phrase _____

16. By whose power is the believer strengthened?

1:11; cf. 1:29 _____

17. Describe the result of such strengthening.

1:11 _____

18. How does divine power enable the Christian to react to testing and tribulation?

1:11 _____

19. If one has been empowered of God, what will he always remember?

1:12 _____

20. To whom can we give the credit for preparing us to accept the inheritance of eternal life?

1:12 _____

21. How are the very first desires of our hearts toward God to be accounted for?

John 6:44 _____

22. How is our inheritance guaranteed to us?

Ephesians 1:13, 14 _____

23. How is it possible that we can become heirs of God?

I Peter 1:3, 4 _____

24. What is the special blessing of the saints?

1:12, 13 _____

25. Describe the realm of darkness.

1:13; Romans 1:21, 22 _____

_____

26. What other blessings do believers enjoy?

1:13 _____

27. Of what does the spiritual kingdom consist?

ROMANS 14:17 _____

28. How did Christ designate His followers in this age?

MATTHEW 13:38 _____

29. While His kingdom already exists, when will it be visibly manifested all over the earth?

ROMANS 8:19 _____

It is sometimes asked: Is the Church in the kingdom, or the kingdom in the Church? The true kingdom of Christ is within the visible Church, a wheel within a wheel. It consists of those delivered out of darkness and truly born again. When He comes in glory, they will be glorified with Him (COLOSSIANS 3:4).

30. What is the price of redemption that has made possible the forgiveness of our sins?

1:14 _____

31. What does "forgiveness" mean?

see dictionary _____

The Eskimos had no word for "forgiveness" and to express the thought it was necessary for translators to use a word of 24 letters. It means: "Not being able to think about it any more." That partially expresses what divine forgiveness means. Our sins are sent away, behind His back, out of sight and forever under the blood of Christ.

32. By whom has the redemptive price been paid for us?

1:15 _____

33. What did Jesus say of Himself?

JOHN 14:9 _____

34. What power is attributed to Jesus Christ?

HEBREWS 1:3 _____

35. Why is it that Jesus was able to pay a redemptive price for the whole world?

ACTS 20:28 _____

_____

check-up time No. 1

You have just studied some important truths about Paul's concern for other Christians. Review your study by rereading the Scripture lesson, the questions and your written answers. If you aren't sure of an answer, reread the Scripture portion given to see if you can find the answer. Then take the following test to see how well you understand the important truths you have studied.

In the right-hand margin write "True" or "False" after each of the following statements.

1. Paul had heard of the faith of the Colossian Christians. _____

2. Timothy told Paul all about the church at Colosse. _____

3. The Colossians were noted for their love. _____

4. The Lord is able to give us wisdom and understanding. _____

5. Spiritual things can be understood with human wisdom. _____

6. Spiritual wisdom and understanding result in a fruitful life. _____

7. Christians are granted the inheritance of the saints. _____

8. Christians have been saved out of spiritual darkness. _____

9. The sinless life of Christ redeems the sinner. _____

10. Jesus Christ is the firstborn of every creature. _____

Turn to page 48 and check your answers.

LESSON 2

Preeminence of Christ

1:16-29

1.How is Jesus connected with the remotest ages of the past?

1:16 _____

2. What powers are even now subject to His authority?

1:16 _____

3. What is said about the existence of Jesus Christ before creation?

1:17; cf. JOHN 1:2, 3 _____

_____

4. Even now, what keeps the universe together?

1:17, last _____

The word for "consist" means "cohere, hold together."

5. Why is Jesus Christ entitled to preeminence as the Head of the Church?

1:18 _____

6. What is the Father's design from all eternity concerning Jesus Christ?

1:19 _____

7. Why is it silly for men to seek "preeminence" in the church?

III JOHN 9 _____

This word preeminence appears only here in COLOSSIANS 1:19 and in III JOHN 9. The words in verse 19 indicate that in our Saviour centers the very essence of DEITY. In Him the fullness of God has literally "taken up its lasting abode." The word for "fullness" means the totality of divine powers and attributes. Any limitation of the meaning of the word which would make it refer only to the past or to the future would be inconsistent with the plain statement of COLOSSIANS 2:9.

The Reconciliation of Christ

8. Why do we have to "make our peace with God"?

1:20 _____

9. How does one receive this peace?

EPHESIANS 2:14 _____

10. In addition to the incarnation, how is this peace made available to individuals?

1:20 _____

11. What is the ultimate purpose of the work of the cross?

1:20 _____

12. God is in Christ reconciling the world unto Himself. How is this reconciliation accomplished?

II CORINTHIANS 5:19, 20 _____

13. Why cannot the "all things" of verse 20 include the one who rejects eternal life?

MATTHEW 25:46 _____

12

14. Why can the phrase not include fallen angels?

HEBREWS 2:16, 17 _____

15. What is included in the "all things" aside from those who accept Jesus Christ?

ROMANS 8:19-22; ISAIAH 11:6-9 _____

_____

16. State the relationship to God of one who is without Christ, even though he may possess an excellent character.

1:21 _____

17. How does alienation of rational powers and enmity of heart toward God usually express itself?

1:21 _____

18. What was needed, in addition to the perfect humanity of Christ, to reconcile us to God?

1:22 _____

19. What standing before God does one possess who has been united to Christ through the new birth?

1:22 _____

_____

The word for "unblamable" means "uncharged." It is a word expressing judicial standing—nonliability to punishment (JOHN 5:24). Believers have their daily shortcomings to be confessed and put away (I JOHN 1:9), but their confessions are those of children at the Father's feet.

20. While the true believer's standing is forever secure (ROMANS 8:33, 34), why will some suffer reproof at His judgment seat?

1:23; cf. I JOHN 2:28; I CORINTHIANS 3:15 _____

_____

21. In what way can a Christian have fellowship with Christ?

1:24; PHILIPPIANS 3:10 _____

22. In what sense were the tribulations of Paul the tribulations of Christ Himself?

I CORINTHIANS 12:12; II CORINTHIANS 1:5 _____

_____

23. To what is the believer contributing in his Christlike endurance of afflictions and tribulations?

1:24 _____

The Mystery of the Church

24. What was the mystery long hidden but now made known?

1:26, 27 _____

It is indeed a startling truth that believing Gentiles can be associated with believing Jews in one spiritual body on terms of perfect equality in Christ.

25. State Paul's description of the gospel.

1:27, last phrase _____

_____

26. What is meant by "Christ in you"?

EPHESIANS 3:17 _____

27. Why cannot living up to Christian principles save one?

MATTHEW 11:28; JOHN 14:6 _____

28. Is it possible for Christ to be in one who is not in Christ?

PHILIPPIANS 3:9; II CORINTHIANS 13:5 _____

29. When will the believer be perfect?

1:28; cf. Jude 24 _____

30. What did Paul desire always to have as the motivating power of his labors?

1:29 _____

check-up time No. 2

You have just studied some important truths about the preeminence of Christ. Review your study by rereading the Scripture lesson, the questions and your written answers. If you aren't sure of an answer, reread the Scripture portion given to see if you can find the answer. Then take the following test to see how well you understand the important truths you have studied.

In the right-hand margin write "True" or "False" after each of the following statements.

1. Jesus was active in the creation of the world. _____

2. Jesus Christ even now holds creation together. _____

3. The apostle Peter is the head of the Church. _____

4. Jesus Christ has reconciled all things to Himself through the blood of His cross. _____

5. Jesus has even reconciled fallen angels to Himself. _____

6. The believer stands holy and unblamable before God. _____

7. The mystery of the Church was revealed to the prophets. _____

8. The Church is for believing Jews only. _____

9. Sinners can be saved by keeping the Ten Commandments. _____

10. The believer in Christ stands before God perfect. _____

Turn to page 48 and check your answers.

Warnings Against Errors

2:1-23

Chapter divisions are sometimes wrongly placed. Actually the apostle is continuing the same appeal. He presses even more the fact of conflict, describing his own ministry.

1. For what church especially did Paul have a great burden of prayer?

2:1 _____

2. What condition developed there, as recorded later?

REVELATION 3:14-16 _____

3. Who else was included on Paul's prayer list?

2: 1 _____

4. State what may well be the uppermost desire of every minister for the church?

2:2 _____

_____

Verse 2 is rendered by Mr. Way: "I yearn that their hearts may be comforted. I want them to be all knit together in mutual love, that love which is the key to all the treasure of the perfect satisfying of our intellect, to the comprehension of God's mystic secret, which is Christ."

5. Where shall the treasury of divine wisdom be found?

2:3 _____

6. What is the only way one may tap this divine supply of wisdom?

I CORINTHIANS 1:30 _____

The word for "knowledge" suggests spiritual illumination, conception of truth. In wisdom we gain the appreciation of knowledge, its relations, practical applications and uses. All this can be gained in Christ, to the exetent that we fellowship with Him.

7. What is the cause of many being led astray from the path of divine truth?

2:4 _____

8. How is one to demonstrate his Christian faith?

2:6 _____

9. List two things we should seek "in Him."

2:7 _____

A tree is planted in order to grow. A building, after the foundation is laid, is supposed to rise to completion.

10. What is an important accompaniment to an established faith?

2:7 _____

Bishop Moule says: "No heart is more vulnerable to doubt and spiritual delusion, than an unthankful heart which will not walk in the sunshine of the Lord." The word for "abounding" means "overflowing," a favorite word of Paul.

The Vanity of Philosophy

11. What is a more serious loss to any person than to be robbed of possessions?

2:8 _____

12. How are many fine people kept from attaining eternal life?

2:8 _____

13. What particular kind of "philosophy" is dangerous?

2:8 _____

14. What is said of a Christian and his love for true wisdom?

II PETER 1:5-9 _____

15. Where does the true philosopher seek wisdom?

JAMES 1:5 _____

The Greek for "vain deceit" means "the philosophy which is empty." Philosophy need not necessarily be vain and materialistic. Wisdom is dangerous only when natural reason proceeds without rule, working on false or incomplete data. When human reason is used to discount God and His Word, it is on the path of pure speculation and certain to fail to discover the highest truths.

16. What word used here proves Christ not only the Son of God, but God the Son?

2:9; cf. ROMANS 1:20 _____

17. Which words indicate that Christ continues to bear relation to the social economy of the great immortal hosts of heaven?

2:10 _____

18. How far does His authority extend?

I PETER 3:22 _____

19. What great class of intelligent people grope in a maze of conjecture without a clue to the meaning of life?

2:10; cf. JOHN 14:6 _____

In these verses Paul touches upon circumcision to show that baptism now holds the same place as the seal of the covenant of grace.

20. When does one get this spiritual circumcision?

2:12 _____

21. Of what does Christian baptism speak symbolically?

2:12; cf. ROMANS 6:4 _____

22. What may one be in God's sight, while he considers himself very much alive?

2:12; cf. EPHESIANS 2:1 _____

23. How does one become aware of the character and claims of God?

2:13 _____

The Ceremonial Law is Abolished

24. What does forgiveness, based on Christ's redemptive work, actually imply?

2:14 _____

25. How was our bond of guilt canceled and our debt paid in full?

I PETER 2:24, 25 _____

Note that the law of condemnation was nailed to the cross through Christ's death. What an expression of substitution:

> He nailed my sentence to the tree,
> The law's decree of death to me.
> And there, when He was crucified,
> The law that claimed the sinner died.

26. While evil powers make a show of Christ in His humiliation and sufferings, what did He do by rising from the dead?

2:15 _____

27. How was Christ's victory over Satan immediately demonstrated?

EPHESIANS 4:8 _____

28. How is the Christian to combat evil powers?

EPHESIANS 6:12, 13 _____

29. Since the bond of the law of ordinances has been canceled, from what are Christians now released?

2:16 _____

30. To what did these Old Testament regulations point?

2:17 _____

31. Who has the right to judge a Christian because he does not keep a certain day as the Sabbath?

ROMANS 14:5, 6 _____

32. What may a Christian lose by allowing himself to be brought under the bondage of the old order?

2:18 _____

33. What is said about the worship of angels?

2:18; cf. REVELATION 22:8, 9 _____

_____

34. If we are members of the Body of Christ, in whom must our spiritual life center?

2:19 _____

The physical body depends upon the head and brain. Volition is communicated from the brain to all parts of the body. The sensations of the extremities are telegraphed back to the brain. There must be absolute mutual sympathy to function properly. So it is in the Body of Christ. Let no man beguile you by bringing in anything that would make Christ less than complete Commander.

35. If we, with Christ, are dead to the law, from what should we consider ourselves free?

2:20-22 _____

36. While the keeping of rules and regulations may have a show of piety, to what do they minister, rather than to the glory of Christ?

2:23 _____

Some might ask, what about the church ordinances of baptism and the Lord's Supper? Neither is to be regarded as having anything to do with the procuring of salvation. Each illustrates an aspect of the Lord's death. In baptism "my death with Christ" is set forth, and in the Lord's Supper "Christ's death for me" is remembered.

check-up time No. 3

You have just studied some important truths about errors in the church. Review your study by rereading the Scripture lesson, the questions and your written answers. If you aren't sure of an answer, reread the Scripture portion given to see if you can find the answer. Then take the following test to see how well you understand the important truths you have studied.

In the right-hand margin write "True" or "False" after each of the following statements.

1. The Colossians were personally acquainted with Paul. _____

2. All the treasures of wisdom and knowledge are hid in Christ. _____

3. A person demonstrates his Christian faith by the way he lives. _____

4. The philosophy of men will help you live the Christian life. _____

5. In Christ dwells all the fullness of the Godhead bodily. _____

6. Baptism is a testimony to our identification with Christ. _____

7. We should let others tell us which is the proper day to worship. _____

8. Christians should worship the angels. _____

9. Christians are free from the ordinances of the Mosaic law. _____

10. A show of piety only gratifies the flesh. _____

Turn to page 48 and check your answers.

Warnings Concerning the New Life

3:1-9

Spurgeon on this chapter says: "It begins in the heavenlies and ends in the kitchen."

1. What is the argument for the Christian seeking the things above?

3:1 _____

Verse 1 is literally "were raised"—a declaration of fact. "If" is not to suggest doubt and would better be translated: "*Inasmuch* as ye are raised."

2. What is the true believer's position "in Christ"?

Ephesians 2:6 _____

3. If a Christian is in any doubt as to what is proper for him to do as a Christian, what effective proposition may he pose for himself?

3:1, 2 _____

4. How are we to discover the things that are above?

3:16 _____

5. What else is involved in getting one's affections centered on heavenly things?

Hebrews 12:2 _____

An understanding of the doctrine of identification is most essential to the victorious life. Christ's death was our death. His rising was our rising. His life is our life. He is at God's right hand, where we also are "seated in Him." We are to seek constantly to bring our present condition into conformity with our heavenly standing.

Believers are Dead to Sin

6. When one has appropriated these facts regarding his identification with Christ, of what can he be assured?

3:3 _____

7. Until what time is the believer's security wholly in Christ's hands?

3:4 _____

One who realizes that his starting point is in the death of Christ and his hope the second coming of Christ is not apt to love the things of this world system (I John 2:16, 17).

8. Since our new life is HIS life in us, what is to be counted as a certainty?

John 10:28 _____

9. What assurance will one have who lays hold of these facts?

Psalm 16:11 _____

Here is unfathomable truth—the regenerate one hidden in the depths of the Godhead. Can a true child of God be torn from that position in the heavenlies to which he has risen in Him? Can Satan seize it? Certainly not until verse 4 is fulfilled. Can Satan overcome Him then? If this were possible there would be no such thing as security for the believer.

10. What is Christ called in addition to "our life"?

I Timothy 1:1; Ephesians 2:14 _____

11. When will this hidden life in Christ be openly manifested? 3:4; cf. I JOHN 3:1-3 _____

12. When we appear with Him in glory, what will occur? II THESSALONIANS 1:10 _____

_____

Mortification of the Flesh

13. State the first exhortation that hinges on the truth of identification with the risen Christ.

3:5 _____

14. How only can one succeed in mortifying (making a corpse of) the deeds of the body?

ROMANS 8:13 _____

15. What must always precede any attempt to control the flesh?

ROMANS 13:14 _____

16. Why should every Christian seek to be free of the habits that characterize unsaved people?

3:6 _____

17. List some of the things that relate themselves to the old Adamic nature.

3:8, 9 _____

_____

18. To what is the old nature or old man compared?

3:9 _____

check-up time No. 4

You have just studied some important truths about the "new life." Review your study by rereading the Scripture lesson, the questions and your written answers. If you aren't sure of an answer, reread the Scripture portion given to see if you can find the answer. Then take the following test to see how well you understand the important truths you have studied.

In the right-hand margin write "True" or "False" after each of the following statements.

1. Christ is now sitting at the right hand of God. _____

2. Christians are to love the things of this earth. _____

3. Our life is hid with Christ in God. _____

4. Believers will appear with Jesus Christ in glory. _____

5. The Holy Spirit helps the Christian to put to death the sinful deeds of the flesh. _____

6. Salvation must precede any successful attempt to control the flesh. _____

7. The wrath of God will come upon those that disobey God's Word. _____

8. Anger and malice are characteristic of the flesh. _____

9. Anger and malice are permitted in the Christian's life if he guards them. _____

10. Lying is characteristic of the deeds of the old man. _____

Turn to page 48 and check your answers.

Virtues Evidence the New Life

3:10-25

1. What is the logical result of relating one's self to the Christ of heavenly places?

3:10 _____

Verse 10 is literally translated "is being renewed"—hence it is not instantaneous.

2. What is said about one's racial background as being a qualification for this renewing work of the Spirit?

3:11 _____

3. If it is entirely outside any idea of racial superiority, what is the source of the superior life?

3:11, last _____

It depends wholly on the perfection of His atonement, the power of His resurrection, the plentitude of His Spirit, the prevalence of His intercession, the prospect of His coming.

The Christian Graces

4. What becomes those who are the elect of God?

3:12, 13 _____

_____

A better translation of "bowels of mercies" is "a heart of sympathy."

5. Why is such prominence given the qualities of forbearance and forgiveness?

3:13; cf. EPHESIANS 4:32 _____

6. What is the great bond, or preservative force, of Christian character?

3:14 _____

7. State the provision that has been made for "putting on" this quality.

ROMANS 5:5 _____

8. List the two important "lets" we have here.

3:15, 16 _____

_____

9. Why is the "Word of Christ" especially important to the Christian?

JOHN 6:63 _____

To let it "dwell"—make a home in us—implies that it is made an everyday intimate guest. It is to dwell "richly"—plentifully—and "in wisdom"—meaning that we study its connections and seek faithfully to apply it. This can be no hurried pastime. Joseph Parker said: "Never gallop through the Scriptures. Go slowly and look around."

10. How only should hymns be sung?

3:16 _____

Most of our hymns are concentrated sermons. Music and poetry may be prostituted to the basest purposes so as to incite the passions, but the poetry of the Christian life is to refine the soul and lift one up to God.

11. What is the "whatsoever" of service?

3:17 _____

12. State the precept that may well be joined with this one.

3:23 _____

13. What is the "whatsoever" of prayer?

JOHN 14:13 _____

The Christian Duties

14. What is the arrangement, divinely appointed, as to headship in the Christian family?

3:18 _____

15. Why does this not imply that the male is superior to the female?

GALATIANS 3:28 _____

16. If the husband complies with divine precepts, why is this arrangement not derogatory to the woman?

EPHESIANS 5:22-25 _____

17. How can a husband demonstrate his inferiority?

3:19 _____

Love includes every attention, honor, service, deference to wishes, confidence, enjoyment of oneness. There is no word in the New Testament that could give any husband reason for getting an exaggerated idea of authority.

18. When is a Christian's work poorly done?

3:23 _____

19. What should be the Christian's ever-present thought to govern the motive of action?

3:23 _____

20. To whom is our smallest work rendered in the final analysis?

3:24 _____

21. What is a good motto for every Christian while at his daily tasks?

3:24, last five words _____

22. What is our sure promise even though employers may not recognize our faithfulness?

I CORINTHIANS 15:58 _____

check-up time No. 5

You have just studied some important truths about the virtues of the new life. Review your study by rereading the Scripture lesson, the questions and your written answers. If you aren't sure of an answer, reread the Scripture portion given to see if you can find the answer. Then take the following test to see how well you understand the important truths you have studied.

In the right-hand margin write "True" or "False" after each of the following statements.

1. The new man bears the image of God. _____

2. Salvation in Christ is restricted to the Gentiles. _____

3. Christians should be meek and patient. _____

4. The Holy Spirit helps us to love one another. _____

5. Singing should be omitted from a worship service. _____

6. All we say and do should be done as unto the Lord. _____

7. Children are to obey their parents in all things. _____

8. In the family relationship the husband is *superior* to the wife. _____

9. A Christian's only goal is to please his employer. _____

10. In the final analysis our work is done as unto the Lord. _____

Turn to page 48 and check your answers.

The Fellowship of the New Life

4:1-18

A Word to the Employer

1. What consideration will any Christian employer show those who serve his interests?

4:1 _____

2. Who is the Christian employer's Master?

LUKE 9:33 _____

3. State a good seven-word motto for the employer.

4:1 _____

A Word to All

4. What is Paul's parting counsel for us all?

4:2 _____

5. For whom were the Colossian Christians to pray?

4:3 _____

6. What was the urgent prayer request that they were to share?

4:3 _____

7. Give a summary of that mystery that Paul always proclaimed.

I TIMOTHY 3:16 _____

_____

8. How are Christians to redeem the time?

4:5 _____

9. What does it mean to walk in wisdom?

I PETER 2:12 _____

_____

The word "conversation" here means "manner of life," or how you conduct yourself.

A Word to Paul's Fellow Workers

10. How is Tychicus characterized?

4:7 _____

_____

11. In what way may Christians be of help to one another?

4:11 _____

12. Where did the early congregations often meet?

4:15 _____

13. To whom also was this letter to be read?

4:16 _____

14. From whom do Christians receive their ministries?

4:17 _____

15. Where was Paul when he wrote this letter?

4:18 _____

Summary of the Book of Colossians

CHRIST IS ALL

In the Perfection of His Atonement	1:13, 14; 2:1
In the Peerlessness of His Deity	1:15-19; 2:19
In the Power of His Abiding Presence	1:27-29
In the Plentitude of His Wisdom	2:3
In the Prevalence of His Authority	2:10, 15
In the Potency of His Indwelling Word	3:16
In the Prospect of His Coming	3:4

check-up time No. 6

You have just studied some important truths about the fellowship of the new life. Review your study by rereading the Scripture lesson, the questions and your written answers. If you aren't sure of an answer, reread the Scripture portion given to see if you can find the answer. Then take the following test to see how well you understand the important truths you have studied.

In the right-hand margin write "True" or "False" after each of the following statements.

1. The Christian employer has a responsibility to the Lord. _____

2. Christians are to be continually praying and giving thanks. _____

3. Paul wrote to the Colossians while on a visit to Jerusalem. _____

4. Christians redeem the time by walking in wisdom. _____

5. Paul sent Tychicus as his representative to the Colossian church. _____

6. Christians are to comfort one another. _____

7. The early Christians met and worshiped in the temple. _____

8. This letter to the Colossians was to be read to others also. _____

9. Christians receive their ministries from the Lord. _____

10. Paul wrote this letter from a prison in Rome. _____

Turn to page 48 and check your answers.

Introduction to Philemon

The Epistle to Philemon is a private letter to a Christian of Colosse (see vv. 1, 2, 10; cf. COLOSSIANS 4:7-9). The letter is a letter of intercession written by the apostle Paul (see vv. 1, 19). The epistle was probably sent at the same time as Colossians and Ephesians (see vv. 10, 13; COLOSSIANS 4:7-9; and EPHESIANS 6:21). Onesimus and Tychicus carried the letter to the Colossians while Onesimus carried the letter to Philemon. Tychicus carried the other letter to the Ephesians.

The Epistle to Philemon seems to have been written about the same time as the one to Ephesus and the one to Colosse. The date given for the three epistles is A.D. 62, which means Paul wrote them while he was still a prisoner at Rome.

Philemon was a rich Christian of Colosse who had been robbed by his runaway slave, Onesimus. The runaway slave came to Rome where he received the Lord Jesus Christ as Saviour under the preaching of Paul. Paul could have kept Onesimus as his helper (v. 13), but he chose to send him back to his owner, Philemon. Paul writes this letter to intercede for Onesimus. He asks that Philemon forgive Onesimus and take him back.

Outline of Philemon (Lessons 7 to 8)

I. The Apostle's Introduction   1-7
II. The Apostle's Intercession   8-25

The Apostle's Introduction

1-7

1. What was Paul doing when he wrote this letter to Philemon?

v. 1 _____

2. What did Paul say about Philemon?

v. 1 _____

3. To whom are greetings also sent?

v. 2 _____

Apphia is a common name. She apparently is the wife of Philemon. The original Greek gives the translation "Apphia our sister" which is not brought out in the Authorized Version. The "sister" is in the Christian sense. Archippus was probably a prominent member of the church in Colosse.

4. Where was the local group of Christians in Colosse meeting for worship?

v. 2 _____

A. T. Robertson says, "In large cities there would be several meeting-places. Before the third century there is no certain evidence of special church buildings for worship."

5. In what way did Paul remember Philemon and the other believers?

v. 4; cf. EPHESIANS 1:16 _____

39

Philemon's Christian Character

6. What had Paul heard about Philemon's character?

v. 5 _____

_____

Paul probably heard these things from Epaphras (COLOSSIANS 1:7, 8; 4:12) or even from Onesimus.

7. How will our love for Christ be manifested in our lives?

JOHN 14:15 _____

8. What attitude should Christians have toward other believers?

I PETER 1:22 _____

9. State Paul's desire for Philemon.

v. 6 _____

The word translated "communication" is often rendered "fellowship," as in PHILIPPIANS 1:5. It would give the idea of "the fellowship of thy faith." The word translated "effectual" comes from the root "energy" or "at work." A. T. Robertson says, "The papyri use this word 'energos' of a mill in working order."

10. List some of the Christian graces that Philemon might have possessed.

II PETER 1:5, 8 _____

11. What was Philemon's attitude toward the saints?

v. 7 _____

12. How was Paul affected by Philemon's attitude toward the saints? _____

Paul undoubtedly refers to his great joy and comfort when he first heard the news of the activity of Philemon mentioned in verse 5. The word translated "bowels" here refers to the emotional nature.

13. List several ways that believers can have Christian fellowship.

Acts 2:42 _____

14. How does Paul refer to Philemon?

v. 7 _____

check-up time No. 7

You have just studied some important truths about the apostle Paul. Review your study by rereading the Scripture lesson, the questions and your written answers. If you aren't sure of an answer, reread the Scripture portion given to see if you can find the answer. Then take the following test to see how well you understand the important truths you have studied.

In the right-hand margin write "True" or "False" after each of the following statements.

1. Paul was a prisoner when he wrote the letter to Philemon. _____

2. Paul chided Philemon on his lack of love. _____

3. The early church met in the homes of believers. _____

4. Paul constantly remembered Philemon in prayer. _____

5. Philemon was a little known Christian at Colosse. _____

6. Paul hoped that the ministry of Philemon might continue to be fruitful. _____

7. Philemon had a concern for other Christians. _____

8. The character of Philemon distressed the apostle Paul. _____

9. Philemon had a good ministry among the saints. _____

10. Paul considered Philemon a brother in the Lord. _____

Turn to page 48 and check your answers.

The Apostle's Intercession

8-25

1. How does Paul describe himself as he writes this letter?

v. 9 _____

_____

When we first hear of Paul, at the stoning of Stephen in ACTS 7:58, he is a young man. Now as we see him again he is around 60 years of age.

2. What really prompted Paul to write this letter?

v. 10 _____

3. How was Onesimus won to Christ?

v. 10 _____

Paul can call Onesimus a son in the sense of "a son in the faith." The terms used are ones of affection and tenderness.

4. How is Onesimus characterized before he was saved?

v. 11 _____

5. To whom would Onesimus now be useful?

v. 11 _____

6. In what spirit is Philemon to receive his runaway slave?

v. 12 _____

7. What could Paul have done with this slave?

v. 13 _____

8. Why did Paul not keep Onesimus with him?

v. 14 _____

9. In what way was this whole episode of the runaway slave turning out for good?

v. 15 _____

_____

A. T. Robertson says, "The word translated 'forever' means 'eternal,' here and hereafter. Surely a noble thing for Paul to say and a word that would touch the best in Philemon."

10. If Onesimus ran away as a slave, how was he being returned?

v. 16 _____

11. What bond did Onesimus and Philemon have in common?

v. 16 _____

Paul is sending this slave back to his legal master, but because Onesimus is a believer in Jesus Christ, Paul expects Philemon to treat Onesimus as a brother in Christ. Meyer says, "In the flesh Philemon had the brother for a slave; in the Lord he had the slave for a brother."

12. In whose place was Philemon to receive Onesimus?

v. 17 _____

13. How were the past debts of Onesimus to be settled?

v. 18 _____

14. In what respect was Philemon indebted to Paul?

v. 19 _____

Paul seems to indicate here that he is responsible for also leading Philemon to the Lord.

15. What kind of a response does Paul expect from Philemon?

v. 20 _____

16. What could Paul be hinting at when he expects Philemon to do more than he asks?

v. 21 _____

If Philemon is to set Onesimus free, Paul would want the idea to come from Philemon and not be based on instructions from Paul.

17. What was Paul's hope concerning the future?

v. 22 _____

18. Through what means might this hope be realized?

v. 22 _____

You have just studied some important truths about the reason for this letter to Philemon. Review your study by rereading the Scripture lesson, the questions and your written answers. If you aren't sure of an answer, reread the Scripture portion given to see if you can find the answer. Then take the following test to see how well you understand the important truths you have studied.

In the right-hand margin write "True" or "False" after each of the following statements.

1. Paul wrote this letter as a young man addressing his father. _____

2. Paul considered Onesimus a son in the faith. _____

3. Onesimus became a Christian under the ministry of Paul. _____

4. Paul could have used the services of the runaway slave. _____

5. Paul was returning Onesimus as a disobedient slave. _____

6. Onesimus and Philemon were now brothers in Christ. _____

7. Paul commanded Onesimus to repay all his back debts to Philemon. _____

8. Paul expected Philemon to take back Onesimus joyfully. _____

9. Paul hoped that Philemon would set Onesimus free. _____

10. The apostle Paul also wished he might some day visit Philemon. _____

Turn to page 48 and check your answers.

Suggestions for class use

1. The class teacher may wish to tear this page from each workbook as the answer key is on the reverse side.

2. The teacher should study the lesson first, filling in the blanks in the workbook. He should be prepared to give help to the class on some of the harder places in the lesson. He should also take the self-check tests himself, check his answers with the answer key and look up any question answered incorrectly.

3. Class sessions can be supplemented by the teacher's giving a talk or leading a discussion on the subject to be studied. The class could then fill in the workbook together as a group, in teams, or individually. If so desired by the teacher, however, this could be done at home. The self-check tests can be done as homework by the class.

4. The self-check tests can be corrected at the beginning of each class session. A brief discussion of the answers can serve as review for the previous lesson.

5. The teacher should motivate and encourage his students. Some public recognition might well be given to class members who successfully complete this course.

Moody Press, a ministry of the Moody Bible Institute, is designed for education, evangelization and edification. If we may assist you in knowing more about Christ and the Christian life, please write us without obligation to: Moody Press, c/o MLM, Chicago, Illinois 60610.

answer key
to self-check tests

Be sure to look up any questions you answered incorrectly.

Q gives the number of the test question.

A gives the correct answer.

R refers to the reference in the epistle or the question in the lesson itself where the correct answer is to be found.

Mark with an "x" your wrong answers.

_TEST 1			TEST 2			TEST 3			TEST 4		
Q	A	R	Q	A	R	Q	A	R	Q	A	R
1	T	1:4	1	T	1:16	1	F	2:1	1	T	3:1
2	F	7	2	T	4	2	T	2:3	2	F	3
3	T	8	3	F	1:18	3	T	8	3	T	3:3
4	T	10	4	T	1:20	4	F	13	4	T	3:4
5	F	12	5	F	14	5	T	2:9	5	T	14
6	T	1:10	6	T	19	6	T	21	6	T	15
7	T	1:12	7	F	24	7	F	2:16	7	T	16
8	T	24	8	F	1:27	8	F	2:18	8	T	3:8
9	F	30	9	F	27	9	T	2:20	9	F	17
10	T	1:15	10	T	1:28	10	T	36	10	T	3:9

TEST 5			TEST 6			TEST 7			TEST 8		
Q	A	R	Q	A	R	Q	A	R	Q	A	R
1	T	1	1	T	2	1	T	1	1	F	1
2	F	2	2	T	4	2	F	2	2	T	2
3	T	3:12	3	F	4:3	3	T	4	3	T	3
4	T	7	4	T	8	4	T	5	4	T	7
5	F	3:16	5	T	4:7	5	F	6	5	F	10
6	T	11	6	T	11	6	T	9	6	T	11
7	T	3:20	7	F	12	7	T	11	7	F	13
8	F	15	8	T	4:16	8	F	12	8	T	15
9	F	18	9	T	14	9	T	11	9	T	16
10	T	19	10	T	15	10	T	14	10	T	17

how well
did
you do?

0-1 wrong answers—excellent work

2-3 wrong answers—review errors carefully

4 or more wrong answers—restudy the lesson before going on to the next one